COVENTRY SCHOOLS'
LIBRARY SERVICE

Please return this b
date st

LONDON • SYDNEY

First published in 2013
by Franklin Watts

Text © Steve Barlow and Steve Skidmore 2013
Illustrations by Jack Lawrence © Franklin Watts 2013
Cover design by Jonathan Hair
The "2Steves" illustrations by Paul Davidson
used by kind permission of Orchard Books

Franklin Watts
338 Euston Road
London NW1 3BH

Franklin Watts Australia
Level 17/207 Kent Street
Sydney, NSW 2000

A CIP catalogue record for this book
is available from the British Library.

ISBN: 978 1 4451 1500 9

1 3 5 7 9 10 8 6 4 2

Frankli

How to be a hero

This book is not like others you may have read. You are the hero of this adventure. It is up to you to make decisions that will affect how the adventure unfolds.

Each section of this book is numbered. At the end of most sections, you will have to make a choice. The choice you make will take you to a different section of the book.

Some of your choices will help you to complete the adventure successfully. But choose carefully, some of your decisions could be fatal!

If you fail, then start the adventure again and learn from your mistake.

If you choose correctly you will succeed in your mission.

Don't be a zero, be a hero!

The quest so far...

You are a skilled warrior, living in a world of enchantment and danger. Humans live alongside trolls, elves and dwarves, while other mysterious creatures walk in the shadows.

The Queen of Alba has asked for your help against her deadliest foes — the Red Queen of Necropolis, the City of the Dead, and her husband, Mortha, the necromancer.

The Queen told you that many years ago Solmor, the world's greatest Spellcaster, created a magnificent crown for the High King, a crown of pure gold set with four great rubies. The Ruby of Power gave its owner fighting skills; the Ruby of Seeing, the gift of telepathy and reading minds; the Ruby of Magic, powers of enchantment; and the Ruby of Death, mastery over the world of the dead.

But rulers across the world wanted the power of the Crown of Rubies for themselves. It became a force for evil and after many terrible wars, the crown was renamed the Blood Crown.

Just before his death, Solmor destroyed it and hid the rubies across the globe, so no one could find them.

But people still wanted them, and now the Red Queen and her necromancer husband are hunting for them. They already have the Ruby of Death. If they succeed in finding the others, your world will be plunged into a new age of darkness.

By your daring, you have recovered the Ruby of Power from its hiding place in the Lost Temple of the Desert. But your companion, Olderon, was not so lucky. He was killed by servants of the Red Queen.

The Ruby of Power is now in a pouch, which hangs from a cord around your neck.

You are looking for the second stone, the Ruby of Seeing. To recover it, you must travel to the mountains of the North and find the Dragon Princess...

Go to 1.

1

You fly towards the jagged peaks of the northern mountains on your gryphon, Hergal.

After many hours of flying, you see the small village of Drakensberg, one of the few places to be found in this harsh landscape. You are sure the Dragon Princess will be somewhere nearby.

How will you approach the village of Drakensberg?

If you want to fly over the village and land in the square, go to 16.

If you wish to land unseen, go to 31.

"I must find the Dragon Lord," you tell the elf captain. He nods and leads you into a great hall. Your appearance causes alarm among the guards, but the elf signals for them to relax.

The elf points. "Take these stairs. They lead up to the Great Chamber. On one side of the chamber you will see a set of iron doors. The dragon lives in the hall beyond them."

You thank the elf, and creep up the stone steps. At the top of the staircase, you see a half-open door. You slip through it, and into the Great Chamber. The room is empty except for a large stone pillar, with thick chains hanging from it. At the far end of the room you can see the iron doors — they are huge! The chamber is full of the smell of smoke and charred wood. As you walk cautiously across the floor towards the doors you can hear a deep, regular rumble. The dragon is asleep, and is snoring!

You approach the iron doors and see that they are slightly open.

To push through the gap, go to 29.

To look for another way into the dragon's lair, go to 17.

The tavern is quiet, except that is for a group of dwarves sitting in the corner.

You head across to the dwarves. "May I sit with you, gentlemen?"

One of the dwarves gives you a narrow-eyed look. "Ha! You called us 'gentlemen'. You must want something, weary traveller."

"I seek the Dragon Princess," you reply. "Perhaps you can help me."

The dwarf exchanges glances with the others, who nod agreement. "My friends and I are feeling a little...thirsty. Perhaps some liquid refreshment would help to loosen our tongues." You smile and head over to get some ale-filled flagons. You return to the table and the dwarf continues.

"They say that the Dragon Princess is held prisoner by the Lord of the Dragons, in the ruins of her own castle."

"The Lord of the Dragons?" you say. "There's more than one, then?"

"Oh yes," says the dwarf, "there's more than one. But the Lord of the Dragons is the biggest, the strongest, the fiercest. They say he is a servant of the Red Queen."

You shrug. "Even so, I must find the Dragon Princess. Will you tell me how to reach the castle?"

"If you wish, but be warned it will take you three days on foot."

You smile. "I have other means of getting there."

The dwarf laughs. "We know. We saw you fly in on that gryphon of yours." You give him a surprised glance. "Oh yes, us dwarves keep our eyes and ears open. My advice is, don't go flying to the castle. The dragons will attack you if you do. Going on foot is the only safe way."

If you decide to take the dwarf's advice, go to 44.

If you decide to ignore the dwarf's advice, go to 19.

4

As you step forward, you feel a stabbing pain. You try to move but cannot.

"What is happening to me?" you ask in a

strangled voice. These are the last human words you ever speak.

Pain flows into your hands. You look at them. To your horror, you see that your fingernails are growing into talons. Scales form on the back of your hands, and flow up your arms.

You drop to all fours, and feel your neck stretch out. There is a terrible pain at the base of your spine as a tail erupts from your hindquarters. Then your shoulders burn, and sprout great, bat-like wings. You give a roar of pain — and find yourself breathing fire.

The Dragon Princess regards you sadly. "You have made a bad choice. Your lack of judgement has been your undoing. The curse that was on me, has fallen on you."

You've been turned into a dragon! Your quest is over. To begin again, go to 1.

5

As darkness falls, you set off towards the castle.

At long last, you reach the end of the bridge that leads to the castle gates and crouch behind its parapet. You spot movement in the

gatehouse and two grotesque figures lumber
into view. Your heart sinks. The gate
is defended by grobblins!

These creatures are a cross between trolls and goblins. They are tough and ferocious, but stupid. You wonder if you can outwit them.

As the grobblin guards stare dumbly out across the plain, you seize your opportunity to sneak round behind them. The gate to the castle is missing and you move quickly and quietly into the castle courtyard. At the far end stands the great keep, the heart of the castle. But your path to it is blocked by a horde of grobblins who are lying about, cooking on open fires and arguing amongst themselves.

If you want to attack the grobblins straight away, go to 46.

If you decide to look for an opportunity to distract them, go to 20.

6

You leave your hiding place and move on. You have hardly taken a dozen steps before a sudden, agonising pain shoots through your whole body. You look down to see rusty sword blades sticking out of your chest and stomach.

Blood pours from half a dozen mortal

wounds. You sink to your knees and darkness engulfs you.

You have paid the price for your carelessness.

Your adventure is over. To begin again, go to 1.

7

You raise your sword in threat. "My quest is urgent! Give me the ruby — or die!"

The Princess raises her head to look at you. There is pity in her eyes. "The Ruby of Seeing," she tells you softly, "is not to be won by threats."

To carry out your threat, go to 4.

If you wish to apologise to the princess and ask for her advice, go to 30.

8

You keep shooting arrows. The dragon roars with fury as every single one hits. But not one of them penetrates its hide. You shoot your last arrow. The dragon's head whips round and the creature snaps your arrow out of the air.

Two more dragons appear, attracted by the sounds of battle. The three great beasts dive into the attack together, each drawing a deep breath, ready to turn you to ashes where you stand.

Go to 32.

9

You notch an arrow to your bowstring, draw back the bow, and loose the shaft. The arrow flies true, but the Dragon Lord's tough scales deflect it. The Dragon Lord awakes with a long rumbling growl. Its head and spiked tail uncurls as it turns its burning eyes on you.

The room shakes as the mighty beast raises its wings until it almost fills the room. Smoke begins to bellow from the dragon's teeth-filled jaws as it prepares to attack.

If you want to stand your ground and fight, go to 32.

If you would prefer to dodge, go to 45.

"I choose the ruby on the right."

With these words, you take the ruby.

Go to 4.

11

You climb the stone stairs to the door of the keep. You march boldly though it, and straight into a room full of armed elves!

You curse your stupidity and haste. You prepare to fight, but as you do so, you know that even the Ruby of Power cannot help you. Elves are clever and mighty warriors, and they outnumber you. A dozen guards draw back their bows, ready to take you down in an instant. You have no option but to surrender.

Go to 33.

12

You seize the spear and turn to face the Dragon Lord.

As the dragon rears up, you feel the Ruby of Power fill your body with super strength. You cast the spear like a high-powered javelin at the underbelly of the beast. The weapon pierces the Dragon Lord's neck.

The enraged beast lunges at you, but you easily dodge, plunging your sword into its throat where the spear pierced the skin. "Come

on!" you taunt your foe. The great dragon roars as smoke pours from its mouth and you push your blade deeper. The Dragon Lord gives a shriek of mortal agony and writhes in fury. You raise your sword to give the creature its death blow.

If you heard the legend from the elf captain, go to 43.

If you did not hear the legend, go to 26.

13

You raise your sword again to battle your way out. But without the Ruby of Power, you are no match for the deadly creatures. Their swords pierce your flesh and you drop to the floor.

The death wraiths close in for the kill...

You have failed in your quest. To begin again, go to 1.

14

You continue your climb, leaving the woman behind. As the day draws to a close, you see before you a rock in the shape of a dragon with folded wings. You approach it cautiously, but this time you are relieved to see that it is only a rock. Reaching it, you look down into a hidden valley.

On the far side of the valley stand the crumbling towers of the castle of the Dragon Princess.

You look around carefully. All seems quiet. There appear to be no enemies in sight.

To head for the castle at once, go to 27.
If you decide to wait for darkness, go to 5.

An elf appears at the door to the keep and stands at the top of the stone steps. You speed up the steps and before the elf can react, you have your dagger to his throat.

"Drop your weapon," he tells you calmly. "I have only to call, and a dozen of my fellow guards will come to my aid."

"For you, they will come too late," you reply. "In any case, I've always heard that elves are honourable folk. What are you doing in the service of the Dragon Lord and the Red Queen?"

The elf glares at you. "I know nothing of the Red Queen. As to the Dragon Lord, we are forced to serve him. Our village is in the forest nearby. Our trees and our homes are at his mercy. What is your business with the Dragon Lord?"

"I'm not here for the Dragon Lord, but I must find his captive, the Dragon Princess." The elf gives you a strange look, and you press the point of the dagger into his flesh. "Tell me how many guards there are in the keep, and where

they are positioned."

"I will tell you nothing," says the elf. "You had better kill me."

If you want to kill the elf and enter the keep, go to 38.

If you decide to release the elf, go to 25.

16

You guide the gryphon and she swoops above the rooftops of the village.

As you do, an alarm bell sounds. Villagers rush into the village square. You see archers stringing their bows, and lighting their arrows from flaming torches. You realise that the villagers have mistaken Hergal for a dragon!

The archers shoot and their fiery arrows streak towards you. Before you can take any action to avoid them, the arrows strike, piercing Hergal's unprotected body.

Go to 47.

17

You look around the room. The walls are bare except for a single tapestry hanging in a shadowed corner. You look behind it and find a small wooden door. You lift its latch and push. It opens without a sound.

You slip into the chamber beyond and find the great room almost filled with a gigantic dragon. The Dragon Lord is ten times bigger than the dragons you have met so far. He is curled up tightly and asleep, with only his back showing, which is protected by rows of tough armoured scales.

If you wish to shoot an arrow to wake up the dragon, go to 9.

If you wish to use your sword to stab the dragon's heart, go to 21.

18

"I choose the ruby on the left."

With these words, you take the ruby.

Go to 4.

19

"Thank you for your advice," you say, "but my quest is too urgent to take that long. Despite the danger, I will fly to the castle."

"Then on your head be it," the dwarf replies. "Head north and look out for a dragon-shaped rock. The castle is close by. Not that you'll ever reach it," he adds.

You realise that it is too dark to set off now, so you spend the night at the tavern.

In the morning, you rejoin Hergal and take to the air. You fly over glaciers and through mountain passes until you spot the rock shaped like a dragon, and the castle beyond. You are near your goal!

Suddenly, you hear wingbeats overhead. You look up to see a flight of dragons appear out of the sun. You urge Hergal to twist and turn in a desperate attempt to flee, but the dragons follow you. There are too many for you to escape! The dragons send streams of flame towards you.

Go to 47.

20

You listen to the grobblins squabbling around the nearest stew pot and a plan forms in your mind.

You pick up a smooth rock from the ground. Carefully, you lob it into the grobblins' cooking pot.

"Argh!" The first grobblin leaps to its feet. "You splashed me, you clod!"

"Clod yourself!" cries the second. "You splashed me! I'll get you for that!"

They begin to grapple and the courtyard

soon echoes with the thud and crunch of
a fight. Other grobblins join in. Soon the
courtyard is a mass of struggling bodies.

The grobblins are too busy fighting each other
to spot you as you approach the castle keep.

**If you want to head straight through the
door of the keep, go to 11.**

**If you wish to wait in the shadows and
watch for a while, go to 28.**

21

You step forward and, with all your strength, aim a sword thrust at the dragon's hide.

But the creature's tough scales turn the blade. Even the Ruby of Power cannot give you the strength to pierce the Dragon Lord's armoured skin.

The great beast uncurls itself and raises its wings until it fills the room.

You turn to flee, but more dragons pour through the main iron doors behind you.

If you want to stand your ground and fight, go to 32.

If you would prefer to dodge and run, go to 45.

22

You stare at the rubies. They all look alike.

"Can't you tell me which one is the Ruby of Seeing?" you ask.

The Princess shakes her head. "Only the worthy will choose correctly," she says. "Make your choice."

If you want to choose the ruby on the right, go to 10.

If you want to choose the ruby on the left, go to 18.

If you want to choose the ruby in the centre, go to 50.

You climb the stone steps without a sound and slip though the open doorway into the great hall, keeping to the shadows.

You see that there are several elves on guard in the hall. You slip the dagger from your belt, and throw it across the hall. It lands in a dark corner with a clatter.

The elves give a start. Two of them go to see what has caused the noise. But before you can move you feel the sharp, cold blade of a sword at your throat. A third elf has crept up behind you.

"When a wise elf hears a noise," says the guard, "he doesn't look for the noise. He looks for the one who made it."

Before you can react, you are surrounded by elvish archers. There is no escape. You have no choice but to surrender.

Go to 33.

24

The dragon soon disappears in the sky. You breathe a sigh of relief and continue your climb.

But it is not long before the creature reappears, along with several others! It was a mistake to let the dragon fly away.

The dragons prepare to attack. You fire arrow after arrow but the dragons' hides are too tough to be penetrated by your arrows. Seeing that you are helpless, the dragons dive towards you.

Go to 32.

You move your dagger away from the elf's throat. "You are not my enemy," you tell him, "except that you stand in my way. Can't we work together? Can you help me find the Dragon Princess?"

The elf shakes his head. "The Dragon Lord is too powerful. You will fail."

"Then I will slay him first," you say. You reach into the pouch around your neck and take out the Ruby of Power. "With this, I can defeat the Dragon Lord, then I'll find the Dragon Princess."

The elf regards you with respect. "I know what that ruby is, but I don't know where the Dragon Princess is held — I have never seen her. But I am the captain of the Dragon Lord's guard. I will tell you where to find him. The rest is up to you."

You nod your thanks. "That is all I ask."

You step towards the door of the keep, but the elf puts a hand on your arm. "Before you go to fight the Dragon Lord, there is a legend concerning him that I think you should know."

If you want to hear the legend, go to 49.

If you simply want him to tell you how to find the Dragon Lord, go to 2.

26

You step up close to the dragon's body. You prise apart the scales covering its heart with the tip of your sword. You thrust with all your might. The blade slides home. The Dragon Lord shudders and dies.

You draw out your sword and watch in astonishment as the dragon's body evaporates into thin air. Where the dragon lay, there is now the body of a beautiful young woman. It is the Dragon Princess!

You realise that she was not the Dragon Lord's captive, but the Dragon Lord himself, transformed by the Red Queen's spell.

And now she is dead. When you killed the dragon, you slew the Dragon Princess as well. Only she could tell you how to find the Ruby of Seeing — but she can tell you nothing now.

Your quest is over. To begin again, go back to 1.

27

You begin your descent into the valley.

Suddenly, the air is filled with harsh cries. Dragons pour from every cave and fissure in the

rocks, and from the ledges where they have been perched, camouflaged as rock pinnacles.

They dive to attack. You shoot arrows at them, but these have no effect. Filling their lungs to belch fire, the dragons close in.

Go to 32.

28

You pause in the shadow of the stone steps that lead to the door into the keep. You watch the windows above where lamps are lit inside.

After a few minutes, you see the silhouette of a slim figure pass in front of the light. An elf! You might have guessed that the Dragon Lord would not want the violent and stupid grobblins guarding his inner defences.

Elves are highly intelligent, and formidable fighters. It is clear you must pass them to get inside the keep.

If you decide to try to trick the elves, go to 23.

If you want to attack the elves, go to 42.

If you want to try to capture one of the elves, go to 15.

29

The gap is too narrow, so you push at one of the doors to widen it — but the hinges are old and stiff. The hinges make a loud creaking noise that echoes through the chamber, and the sleeping Dragon Lord awakes!

This dragon is ten times greater than the ones you have encountered so far. It uncurls itself and raises its wings until it fills the room. Its red eyes stare at you. Three other dragons slink from the shadowy corners of the chamber, hissing a challenge. You turn to flee, but even more dragons appear at the gap in the iron doors behind you.

Go to 32.

30

"Princess," you say quietly, "forgive me, I do not understand. Why will you not give me the ruby?"

The Dragon Princess looks steadily into your eyes. "I may only reveal the Ruby of Seeing to one who has shown his worth."

"But have I not already shown my worth," you protest, "by slaying the dragon and breaking the Red Queen's spell?"

The Princess shakes her head. "There is more to worth than fighting skill. The keeper of the rubies must also possess wisdom and judgement. Are you as wise as you are strong?"

You do not know what to say to this, so you say nothing.

"Well, we shall see. Follow me." The princess leads you to a small door in a corner of the chamber. You climb a spiral staircase, and eventually emerge into a circular room with a small window. In the centre of the room is a table. Laid out on it are three rubies. They seem to be identical.

The princess points at the stones. "One of these is the Ruby of Seeing. All you have to do is choose."

If you rescued the old woman from the flying spiders, go to 36.

If you didn't, go to 22.

31

You land behind a small pine forest.

You leave Hergal and walk through the trees towards the village. You need to get information about how you can find the Dragon Princess, so you decide to head for the tavern. However, as you walk through the darkening streets, you hear the sound of footsteps behind you. You slip into the shadows and wait. The footsteps halt.

If you want to ignore the footsteps and continue on your way, go to 6.

If you want to hide and find out who or what is following you, go to 37.

32

You raise your sword. But a sword is no use against dragon fire. Flames engulf you and the air around you ripples with fire. Your agony is unspeakable, but mercifully short.

Your quest has failed. To begin again, go to 1.

33

The elves bind your arms and march you up a flight of stone stairs. You find yourself in a great chamber. At one end of the room stands a pillar from which chains hang down.

The elves chain you to the pillar and leave. You look up to see a set of huge iron doors at the other end of the room. From behind these comes a deep rumbling noise. Smoke pours from gaps around and between the doors.

The doors creak slowly open and from the smoke slithers a monstrous dragon. You struggle against your chains, but in vain. It is the Dragon Lord!

The Dragon Lord takes a deep breath and opens its mouth. A vast stream of flame belches out, turning the air around you into an inferno.

You've been barbecued! To begin again, go to 1.

34

You snatch a burning torch from the nearest wall. The death wraith holding the Ruby of Power steps forward, raising its sword. You thrust the torch towards it and the creature's rotten clothing instantly bursts into flame. The wraith shrieks and drops the ruby. It staggers back into the other wraiths, and in turn they too are set alight.

You grab hold of the ruby and head for the village tavern, leaving your enemies to their grisly fate.

Go to 3.

35

You shoot arrow after arrow at the dragon. The Ruby of Power seems to guide your aim — not a single arrow misses its mark. But the dragon's scaly hide is too tough for your arrows to penetrate. They bounce harmlessly away.

Now, the dragon is angry. It roars a challenge and swoops down towards you.

If you want to continue shooting as fast as you can, go to 8.

If you decide to hold your fire, go to 40.

36

You remember what the old woman said.

"The higher the climb, the greater the fall,
And right is wrong beyond recall;
Choose wrongly, and a fool is left.
Of wisdom robbed, of hope bereft."

You stand over the rubies and think about the words.

"You must choose," says the princess.

To choose the ruby on the right, go to 10.
To choose the ruby on the left, go to 18.
To choose the ruby in the centre, go to 50.

You stride on, and reach a place where the street opens out into the village square. Flaming torches light up the night sky.

You hide behind a water barrel.

Moments later, half a dozen dark-robed figures appear in the street. Decaying skin shrinks from their skulls and bones stick through their rotten flesh. These are death

wraiths, murderous creatures of the Red
Queen.

You can hardly breathe from their stink as
they pass by your hiding place, and head out
of the square.

**If you want to attack the death wraiths,
go to 41.**

**If you want to head back the way you
came, go to 6.**

38

"If you will not talk, then die!"

Even as the elf slumps to the floor, you
regret your bloodthirsty action. You need to
know how to find the Dragon Princess, and
with the guard's death, you are no closer
to her. Your captive can no longer tell you
anything. You realise that he will soon be
missed, and the other elves will come looking
for him — and for you.

You no longer have any options. You must
attack the guards at once!

Go to 42.

39

You snatch the shield from the wall, but as soon as you do, you realise your mistake. The shield is old. The wood and leather from which it is made are rotten, and the metal is paper thin.

The Dragon Lord breathes a flood of fire at you. You crouch behind the shield, but it is useless. The red-hot flames wash over you, sending you to fiery death.

You are dead! To begin again, go to 1.

40

You keep your bow drawn, but hold your fire, waiting for an opportunity to do the dragon some real damage.

The creature opens its mouth wide to belch fire. As it does so, you loose your arrow. The shaft flies straight and true. Its steel point bites into the roof of the dragon's mouth and into the creature's brain. The dragon drops from the sky like a stone.

You collect the arrows you shot earlier, before continuing on your way.

Some hours later you are heading along a narrow path, when you hear a noise from below you. You peer over the edge of the cliff and see a figure dressed in furs below you. She is under attack by winged creatures too small to be dragons. You realise that the person is an old

woman and her attackers are giant flying spiders!

If you decide that your quest is too urgent to help the woman, go to 14.

If you wish to fight the spiders in an attempt to save the woman, go to 48.

41

You know that the Ruby of Power will help you defeat the death wraiths. You charge at your enemies.

You despatch two of them, but another wraith slashes at you with its sword. You jump back, but the pouch holding the Ruby of Power slips from under your jerkin. The death wraith's blade slices through its drawstring. The pouch opens and the ruby falls to the street, bouncing on the cobbles.

You feel your super strength draining away as the death wraith grabs the ruby. The creature laughs manically and the other wraiths move in for the kill.

To fight on with your sword, go to 13.

To make a grab for the nearest flaming torch, go to 34.

42

You rush into the great hall of the keep, shooting arrows as you go. The elvish guards are surprised by the speed of the attack and several fall to your arrows. However, more quickly appear.

You fight on, but as you plunge your sword into the body of one of the elves, he twists and pulls your sword from your hand.

You look up to see a dozen elvish archers, bows drawn, ready to shoot their arrows. You are weaponless. Your only hope is surrender.

Go to 33.

43

You remember the words of the elf captain and raise your sword. You strike at the Dragon Lord's neck, hacking its head from its body.

You step back and watch in astonishment as the dragon's body crumbles and evaporates into thin air. Where the dragon lay, there is now a beautiful young woman. It is the Dragon Princess! You realise that she was not the Dragon Lord's captive, but the Dragon Lord

himself, transformed by the Red Queen's spell.

The Dragon Princess gasps, and opens
her eyes. She smiles. "Thank you, stranger.
You have rescued me from a terrible
enchantment."

You help her up. "I was told to come here by the Blind Man of the Lost Temple of the Desert," you tell her. "I am on a quest from the Queen of Alba to find the Ruby of Seeing. Will you give it to me?"

The Dragon Princess looks down and shakes her head.

If you want to threaten the Dragon Princess and demand that she gives you the Ruby of Seeing, go to 7.

If you want to ask the Dragon Princess to explain why she won't give the ruby to you, go to 30.

44

You realise that the dwarves know this country better than you. You will have to head to the castle on foot.

"Would one of you act as my guide?" you ask.

The dwarves laugh and shake their heads. "We value our lives too much!"

However, they give you directions, telling you to search for a dragon-shaped rock, which points the way to the castle.

You spend the night in the tavern. At first light you make sure Hergal is safe and then set off for the castle.

The climb is long and hard. For two days you toil up the mountain as the snow gets deeper and the going becomes harder.

After another freezing night you set off again. Eventually, you spot what the dwarves told you to find — a rock shaped like a dragon. You are congratulating yourself on reaching the landmark, when the whole rock comes to life! The rock-shaped head moves, and wings stretch out. It is a grey-coloured dragon!

It spots you and dives towards you. You reach for your bow and notch an arrow to the string, but the creature turns tail and begins to fly away.

If you wish to shoot at the dragon, go to 35.

If you decide to let the dragon go, turn to 24.

The Dragon Lord breathes a stream of fire at you, and you dodge the flames. The timbers in the roof crackle with the heat. You look around and see that the walls of the chamber are

hung with weapons, no doubt from knights and warriors that the dragon has killed. Next to you there is a spear and a shield, but you only have time to grab one.

To take the shield, go to 39.
To take the spear, go to 12.

46

You decide to attack immediately.

You leap up, shooting arrows as fast as you can. Three grobblins fall while the rest stare blankly about, wondering what is happening.

But even grobblins aren't stupid enough to stand still and wait to be shot at forever. The others charge at you.

You draw your sword and more grobblins fall, but there are too many, even for the Ruby of Power to be of help. A huge grobblin swings a gigantic war hammer at you and you feel your sword arm break. Your sword clatters to the ground.

As the grobblins close in, you remember what the creatures feed on — human flesh!

The grobblins have found something for their stew pot. To begin again, go to 1.

47

Hergal screams with agony and writhes in mid-air as the feathers of her great eagle wings catch fire and burn. The flames turn you into a human torch. You share the gryphon's agony as you fall together from the sky, blazing like a shooting star before you plunge onto the unyielding rocks far below.

Your adventure is over. To start again, go back to 1.

48

You race towards the old woman, shooting arrows as you run. Several of the spiders fall to your arrows. The others turn and fly away.

"Thank you," says the woman. "You are kind and brave. What are you doing so high in the mountains?"

"I seek the Dragon Princess," you say.

"Then you must be careful," she warns. "You have helped me and so I will help you. As you near the end of your quest, remember these words." In a soft voice, she begins to chant,

"The higher the climb, the greater the fall,
And right is wrong beyond recall;

Choose wrongly, and a fool is left.
Of wisdom robbed, of hope bereft."
The woman raises her right arm. The cry of
an eagle echoes around the mountains. You

look up, searching for it. When you look down again, the old woman is no longer there.

You go on your way, deep in thought. Was the woman mad? Or will you find that her words have some meaning?

Go to 14.

49

"Tell me this legend," you say.

"It says that the Dragon Lord is not a true dragon," the elf tells you, "but a human that the Red Queen has placed under a curse. The curse can only be lifted if a mighty warrior cuts off the creature's head. In that case, the victim of the spell will live. But if the dragon is killed in any other way, the victim of the curse will die."

Go to 2.

50

You take the ruby. Instantly, the walls of the tower room and the princess seem to fly away.

A man stands before you, and you gasp. It is Olderon!

"Olderon! How can this be? You are dead!"

He smiles. "The Ruby of Seeing gives you the power to see beyond the world of the living. I am here to tell you that to find the Ruby of Magic, you must head to the Sea of Oblivion. There you will find the Old Man of the Sea. He is the guardian of the Ruby of Magic."

The image of Olderon begins to fade.

"Will I see you again, my friend?" you ask.

But before Olderon can reply, he disappears and you find yourself back in the tower with the Dragon Princess.

She gives you a smile of approval. "You have shown your worth. You have won the Ruby of Seeing, but the greatest and most dangerous part of your quest still lies ahead of you — facing and defeating the Red Queen and her husband."

You nod in agreement. Then you call on the power of the ruby again. You see Hergal dozing under a tree. You give a piercing whistle. The gryphon looks up, startled. Then she unfolds her great eagle wings, and takes to the air.

Shortly afterwards, with the two precious Blood Crown rubies safely stowed, you rise on

Hergal's back into the sky above the Dragon Princess's castle. You set your face to the west, and fly towards the Sea of Oblivion and the next part of your quest for the Blood Crown...

DECIDE YOUR OWN DESTINY

HERO

EDGE

BLOOD CROWN QUEST
DEMON SEA
Steve Barlow – Steve Skidmore

1

You have spent many hours flying on your gryphon, Hergal, but now you are approaching the port of Yushan. Beyond the port lies the vast Sea of Oblivion, home to many strange creatures and the haunt of deadly pirates.

You have used the Ruby of Seeing to make your way here, but when you try to ask it where you might find the Old Man of the Sea, it shows only mist and shadows. It is getting dark and you have to decide whether you will continue flying, or land in the port and try and find someone who might know of his whereabouts.

If you wish to continue flying, go to 18.
If you wish to land, go to 36.

Continue the adventure in:

BLOOD CROWN QUEST 3
DEMON SEA

Discover your awesome DART suit weapons systems in Tyranno Quest...

↑ eGun – main arm-mounted, medium-power weapon, fires energy bolts

↑ Needle laser – arm-mounted, light-power weapon, rapid fire

↑ Missile launcher – shoulder-mounted, fires explosive missiles and also QTee's special bombs

→ Net launcher – arm-mounted, fires steel web net to catch and snare

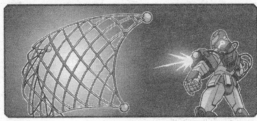

↓ Speed function – run twice as fast over a short distance. Also has "super speed" for x4 speed burst.

↓ NAV system – a guidance system to help you find your way. QTee says, "Use it!"

→ Power unit – storage cell for crystals that you find. New crystals give the DART suit new powers.

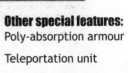

Other special features:

Poly-absorption armour

Teleportation unit

Stealth mode — you can sneak past enemies

About the 2Steves

"The 2Steves" are
Britain's most popular
writing double act
for young people,
specialising in comedy
and adventure. They
perform regularly in schools and libraries,
and at festivals, taking the power of words
and story to audiences of all ages.

Together they have written many books,
including the *Crime Team* and *iHorror* series.

About the illustrator: Jack Lawrence

Jack Lawrence is a successful freelance
comics illustrator, working on titles such as
A.T.O.M., Cartoon Network, *Doctor Who
Adventures*, 2000 AD, Gogos Mega Metropolis
and *Spider-Man Tower of Power*. He also works
as a freelance toy designer.

Jack lives in Maidstone in Kent with
his partner and two cats.

Want to read more "You Are The Hero" adventures? Well, why not try these...

978 1 40830 985 8 pb
978 1 40831 476 0 eBook

978 1 40830 986 5 pb
978 1 40831 477 7 eBook

978 1 40830 988 9 pb
978 1 40831 479 1 eBook

978 1 40830 987 2 pb
978 1 40831 478 4 eBook

www.orchardbooks.co.uk